THIS COLORING BOOK
BELONGS TO:

____

Virginia Beach Goldendoodles Coloring Book

ISBN: 978-1-7362567-0-1

VIRGINIA BEACH *Goldendoodles*
COLORING BOOK

ANNESLEY M. HACKATHORN

Thank you to all of the Virginia Beach Goldendoodle families who submitted pictures of their gorgeous Goldendoodles. Your pictures brought lots of smiles and memories. All of the stunning dogs look treasured and loved. We were overwhelmed with exquisite pictures and sadly we could not publish them all. We will save some for the next book!!!

Grab some crayons & your creativity... relax and enjoy!!!

I LOVE MY
VIRGINIA BEACH GOLDENDOODLE

POLO

Go Dog
Go!

first day of Puppy
KINDERGARTEN

USA

RUBY

We hope you have enjoyed coloring these beautiful pictures of Virginia Beach Goldendoodles.

We started our breeding program in 2003 and have been so blessed to have met so many incredible owners. We continue to provide stunning Goldendoodles as loving family members, service/therapy dogs, and companions.

 STAY CONNECTED WITH US! 

https://www.virginiabeachgoldendoodles.com

 Virginia Beach Goldendoodles

 @virginiabeachgoldendoodles

WE HAVE MORE VIRGINIA BEACH GOLDENDOODLE NEWS...

Look out for children's book,
"SHENLEIGH O'DOODLE, HALF GOLDEN, HALF POODLE".

It is a heartwarming story featuring the very first Virginia Beach Goldendoodle. It is an uplifting story about using your talents and helping others.

Look for this refreshing book on Amazon and Barnes & Noble.

Made in the USA
Monee, IL
20 March 2021